It's Better with

Your Shoes Off

ANNE CLEVELAND *It's Better with*

Your Shoes Off

CHARLES E. TUTTLE CO.
Rutland, Vermont
Tokyo, Japan

To Toby's and Susan's honorary Obā-san

Representatives
For Continental Europe:
BOXERBOOKS, INC., Zurich
For the British Isles:
PRENTICE-HALL INTERNATIONAL, INC., London
For Australasia:
PAUL FLESCH & CO., PTY. LTD., Melbourne
For Canada:
M. G. HURTING LTD., Edmonton

Published by the Charles E. Tuttle Co., Inc., of Rutland, Vermont &
Tokyo, Japan, with editorial offices at Suido 1-chome, 2-6, Bunkyo-ku
Tokyo

Standard Book No. 8048 0268-8

First printing, January, 1955
Twentieth printing, 1970

Printed in Japan

Introduction

We'd like you to meet the Wests. Right now they are engaged in one of Japan's most characteristic pursuits—taking off their shoes—though with less-than-Oriental dexterity. But in a moment they will be delighted to tell you All About Japan.

The Wests are Old Japan Hands. They have lived here in Tokyo, semi-permanently, for nearly three years now. Of course, their Japan is not the Japan of Lafcadio Hearn. It's not the Japan of "Babysan" and her GI admirers either. It's just an ordinary, middle-of-the-road confusion of business, attempted culture, housekeeping, red tape, and the usual international misunderstanding.

The Wests like their Japan. They are getting used to the amiable chaos of their social and domestic relations with the local inhabitants. But they are still on the outside looking in. Somehow, though they took lessons, their Japanese has never advanced much beyond the "Wahta-kooshi-wah . . . uh . . ." stage.

Nevertheless, baffling and mysterious though it often remains, we give you—the Japan of Mr. and Mrs. West

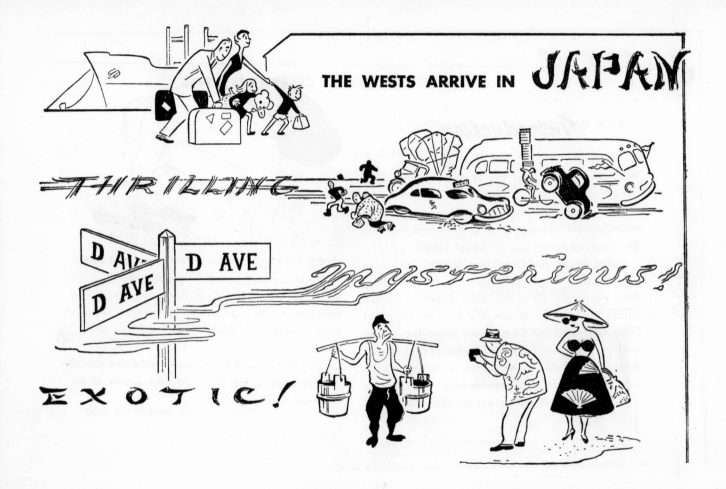

THE WESTS ARRIVE IN JAPAN

THRILLING

D AVE · D AVE · D AVE

MYSTERIOUS!

EXOTIC!

JAPAN ~ A COUNTRY JUSTLY CELEBRATED FOR

the extraordinary politeness
of its people . . .

and the unique beauty
of its landscape . . .

as well as for . . .

. . . those ingenious paper houses we all
learned about in first-year Geography.

Housing is still a problem though. And no real-estate agent approves of Mrs. West's enthusiasm for "the Japanese Way of Life."

"... but we have very-very nice Approved Bungalow."

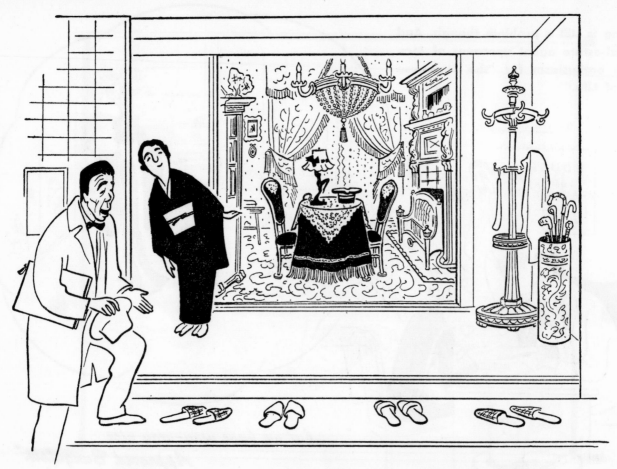

"This is very nice, modern-style Japanese house."

"Landlord only wants to keep one room for his own use."

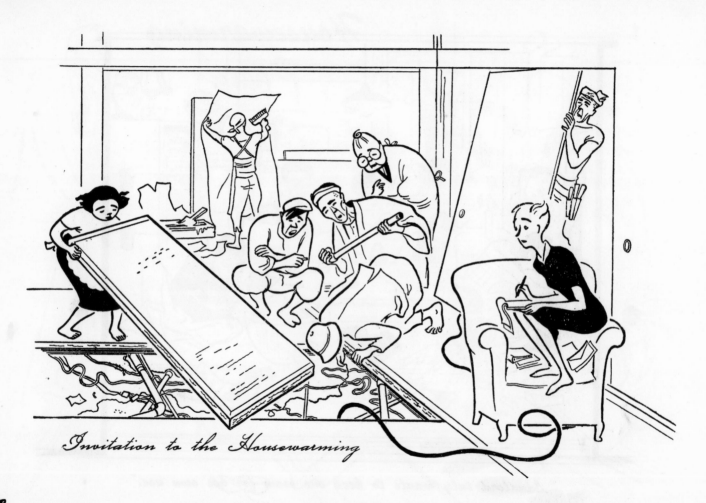

Invitation to the Housewarming

1.

Housewarming Party

3.

Problems of Living in a Japanese House

Mrs. West found that she ended by modifying the admirable Japanese Way of Life with carpets and armchairs and five or six different methods of heating. But there were still plenty of exotic problems left. For example . . .

Clearance

You can expand in a Japanese room — just take out another wall. But don't let it go to your head! Not even if it means dispensing with that beautiful piece of calligraphy which has been in the landlord's family for generations.

The Housekeeper's Room

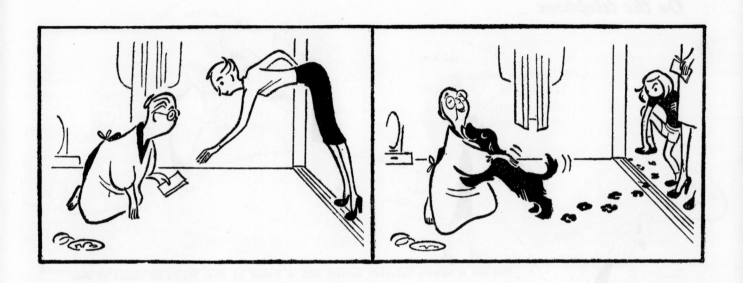

Wearing your shoes on a tatami floor is worse than putting your feet on grandma's sofa cushions. It's more like wearing your rubbers to bed.

On the telephone

Oba-san is helping establish contact with a friend of Mrs. West's by means of that marvelous instrument, the telephone. As she chats with the friend's housekeeper (also a very respectable lady herself), no translation can do justice to the elegant redundancy of her verbs: "Hello, hello"—repeated several times. "Is this madame's honorable keeper of the house speaking? The other day, I am so sorry I committed so great a rudeness in disturbing you with my humble visit when you were so honorably busy. And since then, how have you been? Thank you for the kindness of asking—everyone here has been well too." This sort of thing can go on more or less indefinitely before the whole object of the call—that Mrs. West wishes to speak to her friend—comes up for discussion. And even then there seems to be some confusion.

"Shut that door!"

The art of shuffling a deck of paper doors should be acquired in early childhood. It requires dexterity, judgment, firmness, persistence, and tact—or perhaps you'd better call the maid.

Mrs. West knows Japan is a man's world. But still, somehow, she's sure it's all Mr. West's fault, and that it's ruining his character.

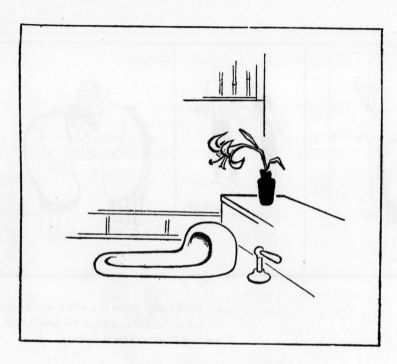

Still Life with Lily

"Convenience place" they call
It in Japanese. And, convenient
or not, it too contributes a note
of Oriental harmony.

In the Shadow of the Geisha
or
Night Life in Japan

First Geisha Party

We apologize to the Honorable Guild of Geisha for this double-barreled libel. But Mrs. West has a fertile imagination where Mr. West's business invitations are concerned.

More Lowdown on
Geisha Parties

A geisha party is like an old-fashioned children's party — very well organized, with games and songs for young and old. Only, instead of prizes, the loser drinks. This keeps the competition from getting too keen.

The Egg and Nose Race

"Good old Watanabe—always a good loser."

The Coal-Digging Song

The Compulsory Entertainment

"Yeah, it must be full of meaning when you know what it means."

*The sad story of a young man who thought a game
of strip poker might put some life in the party.*

STORY TELLER... more children's entertainment, but on
a more realistic plane.

Dining Out

1. TEMPURA, or Fried Fish Dinner. This was invented to prove the rule that Japanese food is served cold.

2. SUKIYAKI, or Friendly Stew. Here it is important to enter into the spirit of what is essentially a cooperative enterprise.

3. SOBA, or Noodle Soup.
This may be approached informally.

4. O-MOCHI, or Honorable Rice Paste.
This is served on occasions
of great ceremony.

5. FRIED EGG, or What Next?

KABUKI
AN INTERPRETATION

We quote from the program:

" . . . being unaware that Nakimushi used to be a general on the side of the Anokata clan by the mane of Norimaki, Lady Kaji-no-Mizu suddenly stabs Sonomama torevenge herself for the death of her son Lord Tamanegi. Surprised as Sonomama is, he persuades the lady of such an inevitable thing as usually done in battle and conforts her.* Later Kumono comes back and tells of Itsudemo's meritorious deed, but without revealing the real fact. Just then Nakimushi comes to identify Ushidomo's head** which he believes is Kumaroku's. However an arrow comes flying to Nakimushi not out of anywhere. Norimaki thus is killed by the arrow..."

*This may be the gentleman raising his right hand. He is obviously a main character because he is much wider than anyone else, but Mr. and Mrs. West have no way of knowing whether he is consoling the lady on the far right, reciting on meritorious deeds, or just thinking aloud. The reactions of

the rest of the cast are no help, since they will continue to register Artistic Restraint until it's all over.

**The birdhouse thing in the foreground is a head-box, without which no serious drama is complete.

"Sore kara, ne— bad Wolfu-san is making
bow and say, "So sorry please.'"

A Few Brief Lessons in Japanese Art and Culture

Let's begin with the Art of Flower Arrangement.

It's really quite simple, you see....

2.

3.

43

4.

5.

"If you were a Japanese, you wouldn't LOOK at the back!"

45

"It seems that's all they learn for the first year."

The Poet and the Petal

Traditionally, the viewing of Cherry Blossoms should automatically produce poetry. Here a bard sets out for his annual bout with the blossom.

1.

2.

3.

4.

5.

Viewing the Cherry Blossoms

Scene in a Tokyo park at the height of the season. The Wests join the Japanese in their communion with nature.

Mr. West and the Festival Dragon

"This picture name 'Momo-taro-san.' Mean 'Boy-born-from-peach.' You see, very unusual because not so many people born from peach."

53

HOME FROM THE CITY

TOURISM

"Well, it just says here it's very old..."

Snapshot Album

Mr. West occasionally succeeds in capturing in his snapshots something of the Mystery of the East.

Famous Statue

View of Fuji

Detail of Temple (Kyoto?
(Nara?

Momma Feeding the Deer at Nara

And Mrs. West is not the only visitor who delights in feeding "those darling little deers." In fact, it often seems that Nara, treasure-house of Japan's ancient history, has become nothing but a gastronomic zoo. The deer don't actually object, though they may appear a little blasé:

"Can't you give them an appetite quickly, Doctor?
Here comes the President Wilson!"

Song of the Open Road

Off the beaten track along Japan's magnificent coast line, one comes unexpectedly upon many strange and fascinating sights, such as . . .

(over)

At the Sign of the Hot Spring

No stay in Japan is complete without a trip to one of the many popular hot-spring resorts. Here, after the bath, the foreigner may relax in a starched "yuka-ta"* and enjoy the magnificent scenery.

*This is usually a little too much for the foreigner's wife, especially when she sees the spectacle her husband makes.

63

MR. WEST was very favorably impressed by an illustrated folder on the

pleasures of the hot-spring bath in Japan . . .

"*Yes, this is our first visit to the Orient . . .*"

Financial Advisor

Shopping

Notes

"Better let me check it for you. You can't trust these people. . . . Let's see now. ¥1,010.45 = £1-0-0d sterling. But the x rate in N.Y. is 2.85 and ¥358.85 is . . . Yes, I thought so — she's making 1½¢ on it."

INTERPRETER

*"Go on, dear, ask the man if he thinks it's enough
for a dress for Mummy."*

Present Tense

This fold of red and white paper means a present. Such folds can be bought in packets of fifty or more at any stationer's, which may give some idea of the volume of presents in circulation.

And at the right, Mr. and Mrs. Watanabe are apologizing for the insignificance of their gift of candied octopus (souvenir of a week-end at the seaside), but actually the value of this gift has been anxiously gauged. They know they are starting a chain reaction which could eventually lead to bankruptcy. If the Wests make the common mistake of returning this courtesy with anything more valuable than a cake or the box of seaweed biscuits they received from Mr. and Mrs. Yamaguchi last week, they will find themselves engaged in a frantic trade war with ever-mounting stakes.

"But it can't be a cake! I'm almost sure she said it had
been in her family for three generations!"

"I look at it this way: Aunt Edith's coffee spoons equal a couple of lacquer things. And that drive to Enoshima could equal three hours at Kabuki. So why aren't we all even now?"

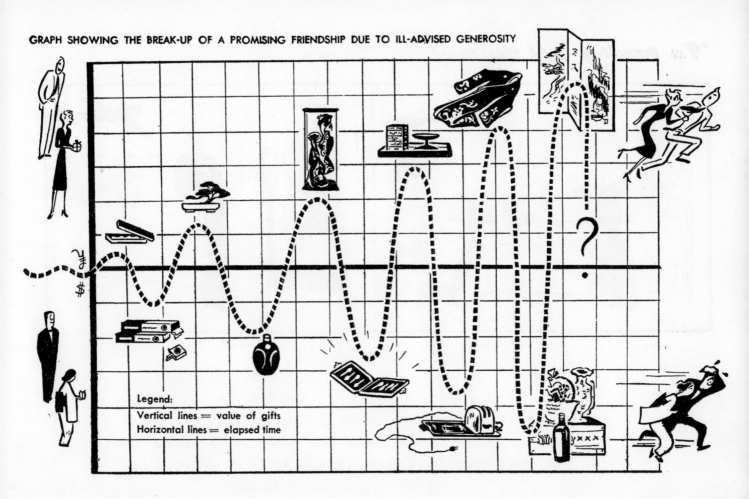

GRAPH SHOWING THE BREAK-UP OF A PROMISING FRIENDSHIP DUE TO ILL-ADVISED GENEROSITY

Legend:
Vertical lines = value of gifts
Horizontal lines = elapsed time

"I'm traveling light this time!"

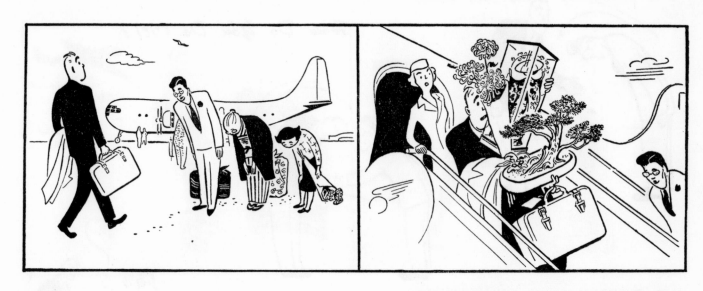

If Mr. West had been a Japanese, his whole office force
might well have come to the airport, in a chartered bus,
with flowers, flash cameras, furoshikis, and flags to bow
him off. But even as it was, there was quite enough of
last-minute Japanese hospitality.

How Do You Do (It)?

2.

3.

5.

4.

We offer this solution — "stone-paper-scissors" — as the desperately needed answer to this daily problem of Bow-or-Shake.

Scene: In almost any public office where foreigners gather.

"Now all we need is six copies of the new form and a sincere apology in triplicate."

Cultural Interchange

Mrs. West's Notebook

Some observations on the problems of women in Japan, which Mrs. West hopes to incorporate in a lecture at some future date to some unspecified women's club.

"What goes underneath?"

Well, under the obi . . .   a cushion ties on in back. . . .

There's a sort of metal thing to rest it on . . .

and some stiffening
in front . . .

and under all this

there's still  *another one . . .*

and so on . . . . . .

This ideal position may be "undemocratic" — Mrs. West obviously thinks it is — but certain occasions still require it. For instance, when welcoming the master home.

"He's a big boy now!"

Here is Japan's solution to one-half the nation's unemployment problem. What reasonable man could object to a custom of such obvious social value?

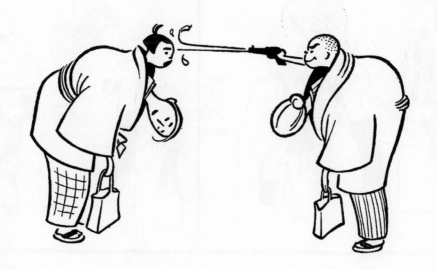

Disarmament

Which only proves that, although boys, are internationally known to be boys, the Japanese carrot is in a class by itself.

1.

Fundamentals

of

Honorable Wrestling

2.

The Last Home Run

Publisher's Postscript

ANNE CLEVELAND (Mrs. A. R. White) was born in Ohio and studied art at several schools. Graduating from Vassar, she became a commercial artist, also co-authoring two books on college life and contributing to the *Ladies Home Journal*. For two years she lived in Yokohama, Japan, where her British husband was in business. They have two children.

We sincerely believe these are not only top-drawer cartoons, but also revealing commentaries on what it's really like to live in Japan — doing for the foreign residents of Tokyo-Yokohama-Osaka-Kobe what the *New Yorker* does for residents of that other wonderland. We are proud to add this to our list of "books to span the East and West."